LIVEWIRE
YOUTH FICTION

The Pride Street Crew
14

You're Never Alone
With A Phone

Mike Wilson

Published in association with
The Basic Skills Agency

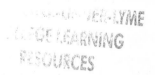

Hodder & Stoughton

A MEMBER OF THE HODDER HEADLINE GROUP

Acknowledgements
Cover: Jim Eldridge
Illustrations: Jim Eldridge

Orders; please contact Bookpoint Ltd, 39 Milton Park, Abingdon, Oxon OX14 4TD. Telephone: (44) 01235 400414, Fax: (44) 01235 400454. Lines are open from 9.00–6.00, Monday to Saturday, with a 24 hour message answering service. Email address: orders@bookpoint.co.uk

British Library Cataloguing in Publication Data
A catalogue record for this title is available from the British Library

ISBN 0 340 77635 8

First published 2000
Impression number 10 9 8 7 6 5 4 3 2 1
Year   2005 2004 2003 2002 2001 2000

Copyright © 2000 Mike Wilson

Typeset by GreenGate Publishing Services, Tonbridge, Kent.
Printed in Great Britain for Hodder and Stoughton Educational, a division of Hodder Headline Plc, 338 Euston Road, London NW1 3BH, by Atheneum Press, Gateshead, Tyne & Wear

JOHN / BONE

WESLEY / TALL

LUKE / SKY

SIMON / CUSTARD

CARL / SPOT.

We all had one.
And if we hadn't got one,
we wanted one.

A mobile phone, that is.

It was cool.
You could carry on talking
to your friends,
even if they got off the bus.

In the Pride Street Crew,
Spot was the first
to get one.

Then Custard and Tall got phones
for Christmas.

That left Bone and me.

I didn't mind.

But Bone did.
You could tell.

He kept asking Carl
for a go on his phone.
Then, when Carl gave him a go one time,
Bone stuck it on his belt,
and tried to walk off with it.

Carl said, 'Hey! What you doing?'
Bone said he 'forgot' to give it back.

Bone really wanted a phone.
He wanted to look like he had a phone.
But his Mum and Dad didn't have the money.

And then, one day,
he came to school
with a mobile phone.
He didn't shout about it.
I just saw it,
stuck on his belt.

'Bone!' I said.
'When did you get your phone?'

He didn't say.

'Did your Dad get it for you?'

'No,' he said.
'I got it myself ...'

'How much was it?'

'Sky,' he said,
'I don't want to talk about it just now ...'

'What make is it?' I went on.
'Can you get *Speak and Save* on it?'

I didn't have a phone.
But my Dad did,
and Uncle Ray did.
I knew all about them.

'Can you do *Text-Send* on it?'

Bone said again,
'I don't want to talk about it just now!'

And he walked away.

As he went,
Bone put his new phone to his ear.

'Oh yeah,' he said.
'Thanks for calling …
What you doing? … Yeah!
Have you done your maths
for Tinky-Winky?'

It didn't add up.

Bone's phone looked good.
It was black and it looked heavy.
It had lights that lit up.

And he talked into it …
Just like a real phone.

But it had a funny name.
And it didn't ring like a real phone.
Not like Dad's,
or Uncle Ray's.

It just didn't add up.

For the next few weeks,
Bone and his phone were never apart.

He talked into it non-stop.

On the bus to school.
In the dinner break.
On the way from class 6 to class 7.

One day Tall said to him,

'Hey, John, let me have a look at that mobile …'

Bone said no.
'My Dad told me not to lend it to anyone,'
he said.

'Tell us your number, then,' said Tall.
'I'll call you later.'

Bone said no.

'I can't,' he said.
'The number is ex-directory!'

Next Sunday, we all went up the park.

We were playing five-a-side.
Pride Street v Peace Street.

We saw Bone coming,
talking into his mobile.

'Hey Bone!' Carl shouted.
'Who are you talking to?
All the kids you know
are already here!'

We all laughed a bit.
But not Bone.

'What are you laughing at?'
he said to me.
'You haven't even got a phone!
I've got one, so you can shut it!'

Ten minutes into the game,
one of the Peace Street team
gets the ball in the face.
He's a Sikh kid called Roop.

Roop falls down,
and starts to have a fit.
We all stop playing and go and look.

'Not again!' says a kid called Scott.
'He's always doing this!
Just leave him.
He'll be OK.'

But Wesley is worried.
Roop is moaning,
stuff is coming out of his mouth.

'We better do something,' he says.
'Hold his head.
Stop him biting his tongue!'

Then Carl has an idea,
'Maybe we should call a doctor!'

'Yeah! Right!' says Wesley.
'Who's got a phone?'

But they all left them at home,
in case they got lost or broken
in the football match.

'Wait a bit,' says Carl.
'Bone – *you* had your phone with you!'

Bone backs away.

'No,' he says.
'My Dad says …'

'Come on Bone!' we all shout.
'Roop's dying here!
Give us the phone, will you!'

Still Bone says no.
He backs away.
'The battery just ran out …' he says.

But Wesley is too quick for him.

Wesley grabs Bone,
and holds his arm in the air.

Bone's feet leave the ground.
He treads water,
like he's in the swimming pool.
Carl takes the phone from Bone's pocket.

'Now then ...'
Carl looks at it, presses a few buttons
'How do you ...?'

'Give that back, you ...!'
He's screaming at us,
calling out a string of names.

Carl is taking no notice.
He's holding the phone out,
'This is … not real,' he says.
'It's not a real phone …
It's just a …'

Wesley lets go of Bone,
and goes to look.

Bone is still screaming
and swearing at us all.
He runs up to Carl,
grabs the toy phone,
and runs off.
Soon he's out of sight.
He's run off down the canal side.

Nobody laughs.
Nobody speaks.
It's like we're in shock or something.

I'm thinking about all those calls he made
in the past few weeks.

The first person to speak is Wesley.
'Sad,' is all he says.

The next person to speak is Roop.
He's sitting on the floor,
coming out of his fit.

'What's happened?' he says.

Later, I'm on my way home.
I get up on my elbows
on the canal bridge.
I can just see a small kid
down there in the dark.

He's sitting on the water's edge.
Looking so alone.

He's throwing stones
at something in the water,
something small and black,
floating on the water.

Slowly,
it floats away from him,
as another stone hits.

Slowly it floats away.

If you have enjoyed reading about the Pride Street Crew, you may be interested in other books in the series.

It's Not the Winning
Carrot Rap
You Can't be a Kid For Ever
She Likes Me
No Turning Back
Child's Play
Damp Dog
Say It to My Face
Who Do You Love?
Let's Go Shopping
A Thousand Reasons
Make a Splash!
Now I Know How It Feels